HOLIDAYS ARE NICE

Around the Year
With the Jewish Child

by Robert Garvey

Illustrated by
Ezekiel Schloss
and Arnold Lobel

KTAV PUBLISHING HOUSE INC.
New York 2, New York

For Ann and Ellen

Designed by Ezekiel Schloss

TABLE OF CONTENTS

Once A Week Is Shabbos

Sunday, Monday, Tuesday, Wednesday, Thursday, Friday — Shabbos.
Six plain days and then the Shabbos.
One day a week is Shabbos.
Friday evening it begins — and lasts all day Saturday till the night.
It is our day of rest and joy.

The Shabbos Candles

Is the cooking done?
Is the house bright and clean?
Have the children had their baths — and are they dressed?
Then set the table, Judy. You help too, Davy. Sit here, Dan — and watch everything from your high chair.
Is the cup on the table?
—and the bottle of wine?
—and the candlesticks?
—and the hallahs?
Then light the candles, mother.

1

Mother lights the candles and says the blessing. Then she looks at her children. "Good Shabbos, darlings," she says.

In a little while daddy comes home. He kisses his wife and children. And his face seems to shine.

Now why are you so happy, daddy?

Is it because the table is dressed up for Shabbos?

—because everyone looks so fresh and clean?

—because you love your family—and they love you?

Is *all* this what makes you so happy tonight?

Daddy pours the wine into the kiddush cup, and sings the kiddush.

Then he takes a sip from the cup and gives everyone a sip.

"Good Shabbos, darlings," he says, and they all answer,

"Good Shabbos, daddy!"

On Shabbos It's Hallah

What do you eat on Shabbos night?
Meat, maybe. Fish, maybe
—but always a slice of hallah.
What do you eat on Shabbos morning?
Cereal, maybe. Fruit, maybe
—but always a slice of hallah.
What do you eat on Shabbos noon?
Chicken, maybe. Soup, maybe
—but always a slice of hallah.

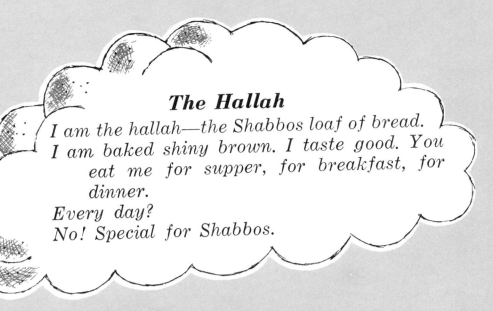

The Hallah

I am the hallah—the Shabbos loaf of bread.
I am baked shiny brown. I taste good. You
   eat me for supper, for breakfast, for
   dinner.
Every day?
No! Special for Shabbos.

Going To Synagogue

Judy and Dave are walking to synagogue with their father and mother next morning, when they see a squirrel.

They stop to watch the little fellow.

"I wish we could take him along," Judy says.

The squirrel cracks a nut, eats it, and rushes behind a tree.

Judy and Dave hurry to catch up with their parents, when they see a kitten with its tail in the air. Of course they have to stop again.

"I wish we could take *him* along," Dave says.

The kitten licks its white paws, waves its tail and walks slowly away.

Judy and Dave almost catch up with their parents, when whom should they see but old old Mr. Cooper!

Naturally, they have to stop to say hello. And Dave says,

"Want to come with us, Mr. Cooper?"

3

"Eh? No, no—I'm going to the synagogue."

"WE'RE going there!"

The old man opens his eyes wide and looks closer at the children. His whiskers tickle Judy's nose.

"Eh? How nice. Then let's go together."

And they reach the synagogue only a little bit after their mother and father.

The Lamp And The Torah

Up front in the synagogue is the ark. Above the ark hangs a little lamp.

"Look!" Judy whispers. "That lamp is on—in the daytime!"

"All night, too," mother says. "It burns all night, too."

"Doesn't it *ever* go out?

"Never. Its light is always on. Day and night."

Judy watches, through her fingers, to see if the lamp will go out—even for a second.

It doesn't.

The light in the lamp keeps on burning.

And look, Dave—behind that little lamp are the Tablets of the Law.

The Kiddush Cup

Do you ever drink wine in honor of Shabbos?

"*Sure. First we say the kiddush, and then we drink a little.*"

Do you drink it from the bottle?

"*Oh, no.*"

From a saucer?

"*Of course not.*"

"*From your hands?*"

"*Silly! We drink it from a special cup, a silver cup, the kiddush cup—in honor of Shabbos.*"

And on the Tablets are the Ten Commandments

    —copied from the Torah.
One of the commandments says:
*Honor your mother and your
    father.*
Another says: *Tell the truth.*
Another says: *Rest on the Sab-
bath day.*

There are *ten* commandments
    —on the Tablets of the Law
    —all copied from the Torah.
Did you know that, Dave?

The Torah wears a silver crown,
a velvet robe, tiny tinkling bells.
"You must love the Torah to dress it up
that way."

Of course we love the Torah! In it is the
wonderful story of our people, of long long ago—
and poems and songs and commandments that tell
us how to live.

That is why we dress it up so lovingly—with
a silver crown, a velvet robe, and tiny, tinkling
bells.

The Siddur

I am your prayer book, your siddur.
Take me to your seats, children.
Want to read what everybody is reading?
Turn my pages to Shema Yisroel . . . Hear,
O Israel, the Lord is our God, the Lord is One.
Want to sing the song everybody is singing?
Turn to Ein Kelohenu.
In my pages are songs and prayers—
for weekdays,
for Shabbos,
and for almost every holiday.

"Good Shabbos, Children"

"Good Shabbos, children," the rabbi said, fixing his talis around his shoulders.

And he read a prayer from the siddur with them.

And he sang a song wth them.

And he told them a funny story and a story from the Bible.

And he wished them "Good Shabbos."

The children wished each other "Good Shabbos," and walked out of the synagogue together.

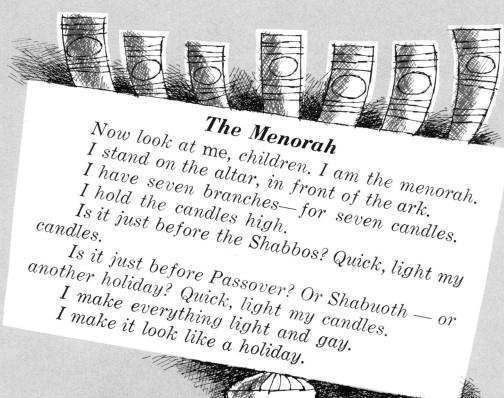

The Menorah

Now look at me, children. I am the menorah.
I stand on the altar, in front of the ark.
I have seven branches—for seven candles.
I hold the candles high.
Is it just before the Shabbos? Quick, light my candles.
Is it just before Passover? Or Shabuoth — or another holiday? Quick, light my candles.
I make everything light and gay.
I make it look like a holiday.

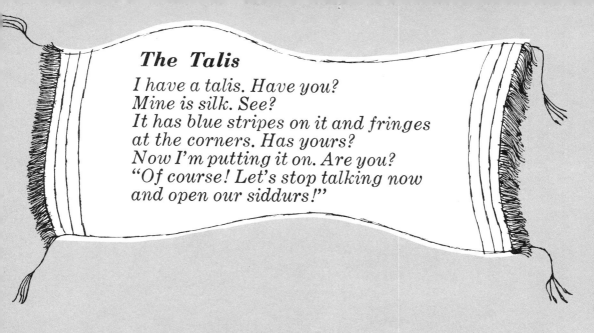

The Talis

I have a talis. Have you?
Mine is silk. See?
It has blue stripes on it and fringes
at the corners. Has yours?
Now I'm putting it on. Are you?
"Of course! Let's stop talking now
and open our siddurs!"

The Sparrows

Judy and Dave came home from the synagogue and found sparrows chirping and hopping on their white lawn.

Eep eep? went the sparrows. *Eep eep?*

"What does *eep eep* mean?" Judy said.

"How should *I* know!" Dave said.

Eep eep? went the sparrows.

"Maybe they're hungry," Dave said. "The ground is covered with snow and they can't find anything to eat."

"Let's get them something," Judy said.

So she and Dave hurried into the kitchen and got some hallah crumbs from the breadbox. They threw the crumbs over the snow.

The sparrows flew after the crumbs.

Eep, eep? Eep eep? they went, hopping, eating, chirping.

Judy and Dave felt good, too.

The Habdalah Candle

Do I look like a peppermint stick?
I'm not, really.
I am wax—red wax and white wax.
On Saturday night you light me.
Before you light me it is Shabbos.
After you snuff my light out, Shabbos is over.
Light me for a little while, snuff my light out
—and Shabbos will be over.

The Spice Box Speaks Up

Wait, habdalah candle — you don't end the Shabbos all by yourself!

First, the Shabbos day itself must be over, and the sun must be down,

and three stars must be out,

and the father must say the kiddush and hand me around for everybody to smell my spices.

Then he must hold his fingers near your light and make little shadows—to remind everybody how different the bright, happy Shabbos is from the plain days of the week.

THEN Shabbos will be over.

Then you wish everybody, "A good week!"

Rosh Hashanah

Do you know what tomorrow is?
Judy and Dave know. It is Rosh Hashanah, New Year's Day.
So they get paper and crayons.
Dave folds his paper and writes on it:
    HAPPY NEW YEAR,
        Mom and Dad! Love from David.
Judy folds her paper and writes:
    To Daddy and Mommy—
        HAPPY NEW YEAR! Love, Judy.
They leave the cards for mother and father on the supper table.

To Synagogue

Next morning Judy wears her new red coat,
Dave wears his new shoes,
Mother wears her new dress,
Daddy wears his new hat,
and they go to the synagogue.

It is crowded. Everybody is wearing something new. Even their faces seem to have a new look.

9

Do you know why?

Because everybody knows it is Rosh Hashanah —the first day of the new year!

See the man next to the rabbi? He is holding a shofar—a ram's horn.

Look—he is putting it to his lips.

Now listen.

Everybody in the synagogue stands up, listening.

"*Tekee-ah*," chants the rabbi, and the man with the shofar blows a long crying note. Everybody's heart beats faster.

The shofar sounds again and again as everyone listens, thinking: *what things have I done wrong that I must fix?*

Now everybody sits down, thinking about this.

The Shofar

I am a shofar
—a ram's horn.
I am blown
on Rosh Hashanah
and Yom Kippur.
My voice is sharp and shrill—like a cry.
I remind you to think:
have you been bad?
a little bit bad? a lot?
Now try to be good.

Happy New Year!

After the service, everybody wishes everybody a happy new year.

"Happy New Year, Dave!" "Happy New Year!" Dave says, kissing his parents. "Happy New Year, Judy!"

"I wish you all the the good things, Mrs. Golden!"

"—and all the luck in the world, Mr. Fine."

"Thank you. As long as we have our health—that is all we ask."

Some people say Happy New Year in Hebrew: "Le shono tovah."

One man shakes daddy's hand and says, "Le shono tovah tikosevu . . ."

"Todah," daddy answers. "Thank you."

"Gam attah," mother says. "The same to you."

Apples and Honey

At dinner daddy cuts an apple into slices and dips them into honey.

He gives one slice to mother
one slice to Judy,
one slice to Dave,
one slice to Dan,
and keeps one slice for himself
and makes a wish:

"May our new year be as sweet as this honey."

"Amen," says mother and Dave and Judy.

"Mm" — Dan says, licking the thick, sweet honey and the cool, juicy apple.

And everybody eats the apple-and-honey.

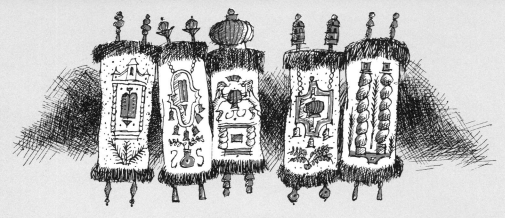

Yom Kippur

Nine days later it is Yom Kippur evening.

Judy and Dave sit next to their parents in the synagogue.

The Ark is dressed in white, and so are the Torahs.

The rabbi is dressed in white, and so is the cantor.

It is suddenly very quiet.

Judy and Dave wonder what is going to happen.

They listen — and hear the sweet voice of the cantor singing the *Kol Nidrai* prayer.

"*Kol nid-rai . . .*" the cantor sings, softly.

No one speaks. No one moves.

"*Kol nid-rai . . .*" the cantor sings.

Everyone is quiet. Everyone is listening.

"*Kol nid-rai . . .*"

Oh, it is lovely to hear.

Next day the synagogue is crowded again.

All day long the people are thinking. They are thinking about the times they had been good and the times they had been bad.

One girl is thinking:

My little sister Joan had nothing to do so she kept hanging around me. But I chased her away and then she was so lonely she cried. I won't do that to her again, ever.

Dave is thinking:

Alan and I have been mad for a long time. I wish we were glad again, I really do. I'll speak to him as soon as I can and tell him I want us to be friends again.

And Judy is thinking:

I thought the new girl in my class was stuck-up. But when I asked her if she wanted to jump rope she was so glad! Me too. I think I'll invite her to my house.

Just then the shofar sounds again, and everybody thinks: *I must remember to do all the things I mean to do.*

And they go home, feeling good inside.

Building the Sukkah

What's going up in the back yard? A play-house? A garage? A kennel?

No, no, a sukkah — a special kind of hut.

Whah-whah goes the saw. *Tonk-tonk* goes the hammer. Daddy is building the sukkah.

"Here, dad," Dave says, bringing him a board. "Thanks," says daddy.

"Here, daddy," Judy says, bringing him a bag of nails. "Thanks," says daddy.

"Dad-dy," baby Dan says, handing him some nothing to build with.

Daddy thanks baby Dan for the nothing. He goes on nailing up the walls of the sukkah. Then he nails a few strips of wood over the top of the sukkah and lays a branch with leaves over the strips of wood.

Pretty soon mother stops in to see how the sukkah is coming along.

"Well," she says, "You have the walls up, yes, and the roof up, yes — but it looks empty."

So she goes shopping with Judy and they bring back the brightest looking fruit they can buy.

Judy hands mother an apple. Mother ties it with a string to the branch.

Judy hands mother an orange and mother ties *that* to the branch.

Judy hands mother a pear, a bunch of grapes, and bananas — and mother ties them all to the branch.

13

"Now it *really* looks like a sukkah," mother says.

"And smells good, too," Judy says, taking a deep breath.

Judy likes the colors and the sweet smells in the sukkah, so she takes a walk in it.

She tries to touch an apple.

She tries to touch an orange.

She stands on her toes and just touches a banana . . and a bunch of grapes.

"All this fruit," she says, with a sigh." It makes me so hungry!"

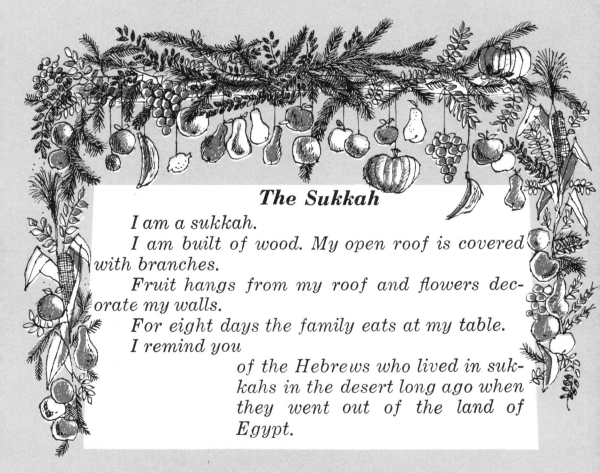

The Sukkah

I am a sukkah.

I am built of wood. My open roof is covered with branches.

Fruit hangs from my roof and flowers decorate my walls.

For eight days the family eats at my table.

I remind you

>*of the Hebrews who lived in sukkahs in the desert long ago when they went out of the land of Egypt.*

A Star Through the Roof

This evening the family has its supper in the sukkah.

On the table are the lighted candles. Along the walls are goldenrod and leaves of red and brown and gold. Apples and oranges and pears and grapes and bananas hang from the branch of the roof.

Dave looks up and says:

"I can see a star through the roof!"

"I can too," says Judy.

"Long, long ago," daddy says, "the Hebrews saw stars through *their* sukkahs—when they left the land of Egypt and followed their leader Moses into the desert."

"What did they eat?" Dave says.

"Well, the story goes that they ate—manna. What did it taste like? It was bitter to *some* people; to others it had *no* taste. But to those people who knew that being free would lead them to happiness, it tasted wonderful.

The Ethrog

I am an ethrog.
I live in a box of olive-wood.
I have a sweet smell. I am yellow. I look like a lemon and feel like a lemon, but I am bigger.
I came from Israel. I came on a ship from Israel.
I came over the ocean from Israel, and here I am, still in my box of olive-wood.
I look like a lemon — only I am not a lemon.
I am an ethrog.

15

The Lulav

I am a palm branch — straight and tall.
Tie me up with willow and myrtle leaves.
Now I am a lulav.
Judy's daddy has an ethrog. He lets her smell it.

He has a lulav. He lets her hold it.
He puts the lulav in her right hand. He puts the ethrog in her left.
"Now wave them together," he says.
Judy waves them . . . and giggles.

Manna

Next day Judy and Dave go into the sukkah again.

"You be Moses," Judy says, "and I'll be your sister, Miriam. And this is our sukkah in the desert. Want some supper, O brother Moses?"

"Yes," Dave says. "What's for supper tonight?"

"Some very nice manna. Same as we had for lunch and breakfast." And Judy pretends she is picking manna from the ground and serving it to him on a plate.

"Mm," Dave says, "Tastes good. You sit down and have some, too."

"Mm," Judy says, sitting down. "Tastes good. Want some more, brother Moses?"

"Just a little more," Dave says. "Just another plateful."

"Mm," they both say, chewing the make-believe manna, "tastes good."

Simchas Torah

One morning — after the sukkah has been up a whole week — daddy comes into the children's room and says:

"Want to march and sing and wave a flag?"

Judy and Dave look at each other, wondering.

"Well, today's the day for it," daddy says, "because today's Simchas Torah."

"Simchas Torah?" Judy says. "Is it something about the Torah?"

Daddy nods. "A special holiday in honor of the Torah."

"Then let's get up and go," Dave says.

On the way to the synagogue Dave says, "Simchas Torah—don't they read from the Torah today?"

"Right," daddy says. "On Simchas Torah we read from the Torah—we read the last story in it."

"Then we put the Torah away?"

"No, no," says daddy. "We read the last story —but we don't stop reading it. We turn right back to the beginning and read the first story all over again—a story about the beginning of the world. Whenever we finish reading the Torah we begin it again. We never NEVER stop reading the Torah."

Flags

See the parade of the paper flags!
We are the flags the children are waving
as they parade behind the men
carrying the Sefer Torahs.
The children laugh and sing as they wave us—
They skip and dance as they wave us—
in the synagogue on Simchas Torah.

Simchas Torah Parade

Judy and Dave are in the synagogue.

Saying prayers? No, nobody is.

Sitting still? No, nobody is.

The men are taking turns carrying the Sefer Torahs.

And the children are parading after them.

And as they parade through the aisles they are singing.

"*Ein Kelohenu . . .*" they sing.

Then, "*Adohn Olam . . .*" they sing.

Then, they sing *The Hatikvah.*

The children parade behind the men, with paper flags — some with apples on the sticks of the flags.

Judy and Dave parade behind the men, too — singing, waving their flags and even skipping and dancing!

Why? Because it is Simchas Torah. And on Simchas Torah we show how happy we are to have the Torah.

On their way out of the synagogue all the children get a bag filled with candy, nuts and cookies.

The Chanukah Play

Judy and Dave are dressing up warm. Baby Dan is busy rocking on his rocking horse.

"Oh Dan," Judy says, putting on her overcoat, "Do you know about Hannah—Hannah and her Seven Sons?"

"*I* know," Dave says, buttoning his overcoat. "They wouldn't bow down to the king. Know about the Maccabees, Dan?"

"*I* know," Judy says, pulling on her mittens. "They were brave. We're seeing them in the puppet play today. Don't you wish *you* were coming with us, Dan?"

But Dan keeps on rocking. He keeps on rocking his rocking horse
because he can't speak yet,
because he doesn't know what they are talking about—
because he is a baby.

Dave and Judy give him a goodby hug and go to the door.

"Don't worry, old man," Dave says. "We'll tell you about it when we come home."

"Goodby, Dan," Judy says.

Dave pulls his cap down over his ears and Judy buttons her coat around her neck. Steam comes out of their mouths as they hurry along.

The auditorium of the synagogue is crowded and noisy. Judy and Dave's friends in the first row make room for them.

Suddenly the lights go out and the talking stops. The puppet theatre curtain slides open and you see the king's palace.

"It's Hannah and her Seven Sons," whispers somebody. "And the king!"

"*Bow down to me, O Sons of Hannah,*" the king says.

"*They will NOT bow down to you,*" Hannah says. "*They bow down only to their God.*"

The king grows angry. He shakes his arms, shouting:

"*Soldiers—take them away. EVERYbody bow down. Bow down to my statue, I say! Bow down, bow down, BOW DOWN!*"

The curtain closes—and opens. More puppets are on the stage.

"Look—Judah Maccabee and his brothers!" somebody whispers.

"*Come, my brothers,*" cries Judah Maccabee. "*Help me chase away the king's soldiers.*" And they pick up sticks and stones and chase away the soldiers.

"*Hurray!*" shout the people. "*Hurray for the Maccabees. They chased away the soldiers! Now let us clean the Temple and light the Temple lamp again.*"

The curtain closes, the children clap hands wildly, and the lights go on in the auditorium.

And After

It is snowing.

The snowflakes tickle Judy's neck, so she buttons her collar.

Dave scoops up some snow and makes a snowball. He throws it at a tree.

"Look at me," he calls out. "I'm Judah Maccabee! I'm chasing away the king's soldiers."

"Come *on!*" cries Judy. "It's co-o-old."

Home again for dinner, Judy and Dave tell all about the puppet play.

Judy tells about Hannah. Dave tells about the Maccabees. Dan, in his high chair, clanks his spoon on his plate.

After dinner, Dave and Judy go to their playroom. They get out crayons and paste and scissors and start making Chanukah cards.

They hide the cards when their mother comes in. They want the cards to be a surprise.

Hurray For H-Hannah

Dave looks out of the window. It has stopped snowing.

"Let's make a snowman," he says.

So he and Judy put on their overcoats and mittens and go out. They make a snowman—with a big fat face and licorice drops for eyes.

"This snowman is the king," Dave says.

"Let's make a snow-woman," Judy says, "Hannah!"

So they make a snow-woman—with a gum-drop for a mouth.

Dave shouts:

"The king says—'BOW DOWN!'"

Judy shouts back:

"Hannah says—'No!'"

"Now I'm Judah Maccabee," Dave says. "We will NOT bow down to you, you stupidhead crazy king. Bow down YOURSELF!" And he knocks the king's snow head off. Then, shouting, "Hurray for Judah Maccabee!" he runs and slides on the snow.

"Hurray for H-Hannah!" Judy says in a little voice, shivering. "Let's g-go *in* now, Davy. Please!"

Judah Maccabee

I am Judah Maccabee.

The king is putting his statue in our Temple. If they do not bow down, he is having them killed.

Let us fight this cruel king.

Let us show the people how to fight this king and his soldiers.

Come, my brothers!

Chanukah Presents

Daddy is home now.

The family stands around the menorah. Judy is watching her daddy and listening to him. Dave is worried. He can't see any packages . . .

"On the first night of Chanukah, we light one candle," daddy says. And he sings the Chanukah blessing and touches the candle in the menorah with the lighted shammash candle, lighting it.

"*Mo-Oz tsur ye-shu-osi . . .*" everybody sings.

When the singing is over, daddy says, "Good Yom Tov."

"Good Yom Tov, daddy," everybody says. "Good Yom Tov, Dave." "Good Yom Tov, Judy." "Good Yom Tov, Mommy."

And everybody kisses everybody.

Daddy puts the menorah on the window sill so anybody passing in the street can see its light too.

Dave still can't think where the presents might be. Judy whispers, "Let's get the cards," and they go for them.

When they bring the cards back, something seems to be different in the room. They give the cards to their parents and Dan.

"How lovely," mother says. "Beautiful." daddy says. Dan, very happy, tries to eat his. Suddenly there is a new *sound* in the room: *"Erf-erf!"*

And in a little box in the corner of the room is a brown-and-white puppy!

The children shriek for joy, pick him up together and try to cuddle him.

His nose is wet and his tail is shivering and he licks their faces.

"Put him back now, children, and let's wash and sit down for supper," mother says, at last.

Spinning The Dreidel

While everybody is at supper, with the children looking at the box every minute to make sure their puppy is all right, the bell rings. In comes grandma and grandpa.

"Good Yom Tov," they say. "Good appetite."

The children run to them and hug them before they can get their cold coats off. "We got a puppy!" Dave shrieks at them. "Want to see him?" cries Judy. "Look, I'll show you."

"*Really?*" says grandpa, following her to the box.

"I hope we're not too late," grandma says, handing a package to mommy.

"Latkes! Never too late, mother."

And everybody soon has at least one of grandma's latkes—the special pancakes that she makes every year for Chanukah.

After supper, grandpa has a little talk with the children and the puppy, who has gotten very tired and gone to sleep in his little box bed. Then grandpa takes something out of his pocket.

"Chanukah gelt," he says, putting three shiny dimes into Dave's hand and three shiny dimes into Judy's hand. Out of his other pocket he takes a dreidel.

Judy spins the dreidel, then Dave spins it. Around it goes until it wobbles to a stop.

"Now, *I*'ll be a dreidel," Dave says. And he spins around and around till the room is spinning too, and so are the table and chairs and the puppy box and mommy and daddy and grandpa and grandma and the ceiling. He lands on the floor, quite dizzy.

"Oh!" he says, trying to climb off the floor.

"Now—how about *playing* dreidel," grandpa says.

And he digs into his overcoat pocket and pulls out a bag of nuts and raisins. He gives some to Dave and some to Judy. Then he sits down on the floor and shows them how to play.

Grandma looks at mommy and daddy. "See?" she says. "Chanukah makes grandpa young again."

After a while, mommy says, "Tomorrow's another day."

"Tomorrow?"

"Well, tomorrow night we light *two* candles."

"Can I light one tomorrow night?" Judy says. "And me?" Dave says.

"Judy tomorrow. And the next night, Dave."

"And there'll be another present tomorrow night," mother says.

Dave and Judy hug everybody goodnight. They bring their sleeping puppy a dish of fresh water, take a last loving look at him and go off to bed.

"Good night, children."

The Dreidel

I am a dreidel—a Chanukah top.
On my sides are four letters—Nun, Gimel,
Hay and Shin.
They stand for Nes Gadol Hayah Shom . . .
"A Great Miracle Happened There."
Spin me and around I go.
Now watch me go slower . . slower . . and . .
Look—see what letter I stopped on!
Did you win?

Light Me and Watch Me

I am a Chanukah candle.
Light me and watch me. Watch me and sing:
Mo-oz tsur ye-shu-osi.
Tonight you light one; tomorrow, two.
Then you light three, and the next night four.
When you light all eight—how bravely we
   shine and flicker!
And you think of Hannah and her brave sons.
And you think of Judah and his brave brothers.
And of the people who would not bow down
   to the king's statue.
And you think of the eight days of thanks-
   giving in the Temple
             and the little lamp that burned
                for eight days long, long ago.
So light me and watch me; watch me and sing,
Mo-oz tsur ye-shu-osi.

The Shammash Candle

I am the shammash candle.
Light me and I will light the others.
Help me and I will help my brothers.
See how I pass on the light? That's my job.

Hannah

I am Hannah. And you are my seven sons.
When the king says, "Bow down to me!" do not bow down. Be brave. Tell him you bow down only to your God. Are you ready, my sons? Let us go to the king and tell him.

The King

I am the king. People say I am cruel.
I am NOT cruel. I just want everybody to do what I tell them. Bow down to me, O sons of Hannah. What? You will not bow down? Then you shall all be killed! And I shall put my statue in your Temple—and MAKE everybody bow down to it!

The People

Hurrah for the Maccabees, we say.

They are brave—and they showed us how to be brave.

They showed us how to fight the wicked king and his soldiers.

We won the fight and we are free again.

Now let us clean the Temple and throw out the statue of the king.

Let us dance and sing and feast.

Come, let us find some oil and light the holy lamp.

Little Jar of Oil

I am a little jar of oil. I am in the Temple, long, long ago.

Everyone thinks I will burn for one day. But I will burn for eight days.

And everybody will dance and laugh and sing:

"Instead of one day, eight days,
Instead of one night, eight nights!"

Now you light little Chanukah candles in your home.

For one night?
EIGHT nights!

Happy New Year, Trees

In school the teacher gave each child a picture—

>a picture of an orange tree,
>an olive tree,
>a fig tree,
>a eucalyptus tree,
>a palm tree,

and other trees that grow in Israel.

I wonder what this tree is good for, Judy was thinking.

Under her picture she read:

If you want to get out of the hot sun, just sit in my shade. You'll find it cool and comfortable.

Now what good are you, Dave thought, looking at his picture.

And he read: *Once it was swampy here. But somebody planted me and my roots drank up the swamp. Now the ground is clean and dry.*

And all the children looking at their pictures thought, What good are you—and you—and you.

And they read: *You can eat my oranges . . .* or *You can eat my dates . . .* or *You can eat my figs . . .* or *You can eat my carob fruit.*

"Now what do you think of trees?" the teacher said.

"They're a very good idea," Dave said.

The other children laughed, and somebody said, "Hooray for trees! Happy New Year, trees!"

"Happy New Year, trees!" said everybody.

And the teacher said: "Grow big and strong, trees. And have leaves and blossoms and fruit!"

Chamisho Oser B'Shvat

Later, in the auditorium, Judy and Dave saw movies of children who lived in Israel. The children there had a holiday from school on Chamisho Oser and were planting new trees.

The lights went on.

"It is spring in Israel on this New Year's Day for Trees," the principal said. "But here it is winter. The ground is hard. It is too cold to plant trees. But we can start a little plant in this window box. Who would like to come up and help me?"

Up went Judy's hand — the first hand up.

So she walked up on the stage. In front of all the children she helped the principal plant a plant.

Before the children left the auditorium they got something sweet that grows in Israel.

What did they get?

Pomegranates.

   dates,

      carob fruit,

         figs.

And so did Judy and Dave.

They each got a bagful of dates, pomegranates, carob fruit, raisins, and figs.

HAPPY NEW YEAR, TREES!

Reading the Megillah

One morning Dave woke up, rubbed his eyes and smiled.

Do you know why he was smiling?

Because he remembered it was Purim. And Purim is the day you have FUN —

giving presents,
hearing the megillah,
whirling a gragger,
going to a masquerade party,
eating hamantaschen,
seeing a play.

No wonder Dave smiled.

"Hurry down!" Judy called to her brother. "We're going to the synagogue — to hear them read the megillah."

"I'm hurrying," Dave said, putting both his legs into one trouser and then trying to put his right shoe on his left foot. "I'm *hurrying!*"

At the synagogue the children were given graggers.

One child got a gragger you whirl,
another got a gragger you shake,
another got a gragger you rattle.

The Reader began reading the megillah — *The Book of Esther*. The children held their graggers ready, waiting for the name 'Haman'.

31

The Reader pointed to the words of the megillah with a silver pointer. He chanted: *Once there was a wicked man. He wanted to harm the Jews, but Queen Esther heard about it, told the King, and the King punished this wicked man whose name was Haman—*

HAMAN?

Judy shook her gragger, Dave whirled his gragger, and other children rattled theirs and made all the noise they could—to drown out the name of that wicked man.

The Megillah

I am The Book of Esther.
I am written on a scroll that you unwind as you read.
Read me in the synagogue. Point to my words with a silver pointer.
Once there was a wicked man. He wanted to harm the Jews, but Queen Esther heard about it and told the King and the King punished him.
Read me on Purim. I am that story.

The Gragger Speaks

Whirl me, shake me, rattle me.
Do you know what I am?
I am a Purim gragger.
I make a noise.
I make a noise, you know, to drown out the
name of that wicked man, Haman.
Quick—quick! Whirl me, shake me, rattle me
—I JUST HEARD 'HAMAN'!
R-r-rat-tatee-grackety gracket — bing bang
BOOM!

Shalach Manoth

On the way home from synagogue, Judy and
Dave kept skipping ahead of their father.

"Say 'Haman'," Judy would say. When Dave
said it, she would shake her gragger.

"Say 'Haman,'" Davy would say. When she
said it, he'd whirl his gragger.

For dinner that day mother had roasted a
turkey. And grandma had sent over kreplach
for the soup and hamantaschen for dessert.

After dinner, the children dressed up.

Dave put on a long gown that made him look
like Mordecai, and a mask to hide his face. On his
arm he had a basket with hamantaschen.

Judy put on a crown that made her look like Queen Esther, and a mask to hide her face. On her arm she had a basket of hamantaschen.

Then they went out. They went to the house next door.

"Is Alan home, Mrs. Rubin?" Judy asked the woman who opened the door.

"No, he's out," Mrs. Rubin said. "Taking shalach manoth around. Now wait a moment." And she went into the house and came out again.

"This," she said, giving them five cents each, "is money for the poor." "And this," she said, dropping a bag of goodies into each basket, "is shalach manoth for Queen Esther and shalach manoth for Cousin Mordecai."

Judy giggled and so did Dave. In fact, they giggled so much they forgot to say "Good Purim." They just took hamantaschen from their baskets and put them into Mrs. Rubin's hand.

"Thank you — for Alan," Mrs. Rubin said. "And Good Purim!"

After leaving hamantaschen at other friends' houses, Judy and Dave came home.

They put down their heavy baskets, filled with new goodies, and they emptied all the Purim money into their charity box.

"Now let's hurry," Judy said, "or we'll be late for the masquerade party."

And off they went.

Purim Party

At the masquerade party were ten Mordecais, twelve Esthers, 5 Kings, 3 Hamans, a hamantasch and a king's horse.

The music played, the judges looked on, and everybody paraded around the room.

Then prizes were given out to the child who was

the prettiest,
the silliest,
the fattest,
the tallest,
the littlest,
the funniest.

EVERYBODY got a prize.

And the king's horse got TWO prizes — one prize to the boy working the head, and one prize to the boy swishing the tail.

After the children took off their masks, they shook hands

and sang Purim songs,
and played games,
and danced in a circle,
and watched the puppet play.

Hamantasch, Hamantasch

I am a hamantasch.
I have three corners.
Sometimes I am filled
with poppy seeds.
Sometimes I am filled
with chopped prunes
and raisins.
I taste good.
Eat me on Purim.

People in the Puppet Play

I am Vashti. I was the queen of all Persia. I told the king I would not go to his party. That made him angry. So he chose a new queen — Esther.

I am Haman, the king's Prime Minister. Everybody bows down to me — except Mordecai the Jew. Mordecai must bow down to me, too, I say. If he will not bow down I shall get even with him. And I shall get even with his people.

I am Mordecai. I must save my people from Haman. I shall ask my cousin Esther, the queen, to help. And I shall tell my people to be brave.

I am Queen Esther. Mordecai just told me about the wicked plan of Haman. Oh, dear! I must tell my husband, the king, about it.

I am Ahasueras, king of all Persia. Esther has told me about Haman. He wants to harm her people. I will not let him. They are good people. Soldiers, arrest Haman. Now, good people, do not be afraid.

We are the Jews of Persia. We are proud of Queen Esther. She helped save us from harm. Hurrah for our queen! And hurrah for Mordecai!

Do You Like – Matzoth?

Judy said to her friend, Ruth:

"Do you like parties?"

"Sure," said Ruth.

"So do I," said Judy. "Do you like to hear stories and do you like to sing?"

"Of course," said Ruth.

"So do I. Do you like — matzoth?"

"M-m-m," said Ruth.

"Me, too. Do you like — when it's Passover?"

"I don't know. What do you do when it's Passover?"

"You have a party — for the whole family. You sing songs and you hear stories and you eat matzoth. Do you like — when it's Passover?"

"Oh, yes."

"SO DO I."

Here Comes Passover

Scrub your floors,
Sweep your house,
Change your dishes,
Put on new clothes —
Here — comes — PASSOVER.

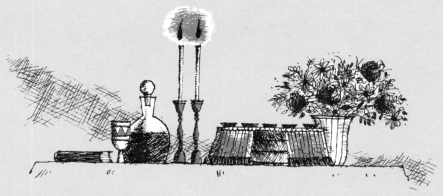

Ready For Passover

It was nearly Passover.

Daddy had cleaned the rugs. Mother had washed all the Passover dishes and put them away in the cupboard.

She lay a clean white cloth over the table and went back to the kitchen.

"Now," she said, "let's dress up the table for the seder. Davy, will you take in the candlesticks? Here, Judy, are the knives and forks."

Soon the table was dressed up with the shiny candlesticks and the bottle of wine and wine glasses

and the seder plate of charoses and maror

and the plate of matzoth, with fancy cover.

Then everybody washed and dressed.
Mother put on her new dress.
Daddy put on his best suit.
Judy put on her new red shoes.
Dave put on *his* new shoes.
And baby Dan had a new bib on.
Now everybody was dressed
for the seder.

If A Matzah Could Talk

I am a matzah.
I live in a box with my brothers.
My brothers are square, and so am I.
My brothers are crisp, and so am I.
My brothers are good to eat, and so am I.
Eat me now, eat me tomorrow, eat me all week.

Eat me with butter, eat me with honey, eat me with jam — but PLEASE EAT ME!

Tonight Is Passover

What do you know?
Tonight is Passover — that's what I know.
What will you do?
*I'll sit at the seder — that's what I'll do. I'll
ask the Four Questions and sing with everybody
and I'll sip four glasses of wine — that's what I'll
do.*

And what will you eat?
Matzah — that's what I'll eat
        — and a little bit of maror
        — and a little bit of charoseth
        *— and a hard-boiled egg in salt
        water*
        that's what I'll eat.

The Seder

Daddy filled everybody's glass with wine.

He lifted his own wine cup and sang the kiddush — the same kiddush that Jews have sung for hundreds of years — and he drank from his cup.

Mother and Judy and Dave, too, drank a little from their glasses.

Then Judy and Dave asked the Four Questions that were in the haggadah.

"Mah Nishtanah," David said. "Why is tonight different from all other nights? Tonight we eat matzah. Why?"

"Tonight we eat maror, bitter herbs," said Judy. "Why?"

And Dave said: "Tonight we dip the herbs into salt water. Why?"

And Judy said: "Tonight we eat our supper leaning, kind of. Why?"

"You mean leaning like this?" daddy said. "Taking it easy? This is to show that I'm a free man."

"What's free?" Dave said. "For nothing?"

"Am *I* free?" Judy said.

Daddy nodded. "Everybody at this table is free — free to do what we want. We can eat together and joke and laugh. We're free to go to school, to work, to rest. We all have time to play, too, and sing and dance, if we want to. But once upon a time . . ." he read from the haggadah, "long, long ago, our great-great-great-great-great-grandparent Hebrews were not free. They lived in the land of Egypt and they were slaves — slaves of Pharaoh the king. . .

They had to work hard from morning till night — every day. They could not stop to rest when they were tired. They had no time to spend with their children — no time to teach them, no time to play with them. They had to work all day long and part of the night, too. They had to make bricks and build his gigantic pyramids. Their lives were hard, their lives were bitter.

Now, in the palace was a man, Moses, who was a Hebrew himself. He went to Pharaoh and said:

"O Pharaoh, my people do not want to be your slaves. They want to be free. Let my people go away from here."

After a long while Pharaoh said, "Very well. Your people may go."

But after he let them go, he thought, "Now who will slave for me? Who will build my gigantic pyramids?"

So he shouted after them to come back. He even sent soldiers on horses and chariots after them. But the Hebrews kept on going because they wanted to be free. All the king's horses and all the king's men could not stop them. They kept on going until they were out of the land of Egypt.

Now Pharaoh's soldiers could never catch them.

Now the Hebrews weren't slaves.
They could stop at a well and drink.
They could rest under the palm trees.
They could play with their children.
They could sing together and dance together.
Now they were free.

When the Hebrews left the land of Egypt,
they took blankets of straw and jars and plates,
and dough they had just mixed,
and they hurried away with Moses.

When they came to the edge of the desert they
stopped to rest.

The sun was very hot. It baked the dough into
a hard bread — matzah.

So the people ate this hard bread, matzah —
instead of ordinary bread.

We too eat matzah on Passover — and it reminds us of that time, long long ago when our
great-great-great-great-great-grandparents were
slaves in the land of Egypt and their lives were
hard. And it reminds us of the time they hurried
out of the land of Egypt to be free.

"Here," daddy said, giving everyone a piece
of matzah.

Then he said the matzah blessing — the same
one that Jews have said for hundreds of years.
And everybody ate the matzah.

So did baby Dan. Only he was eating his piece
of matzah all evening.

The Haggadah

I am the haggadah — the book about Passover.

Is the seder tonight?

Then read my words and look at my pictures.
I tell you the wonderful story of the Hebrews and how they left the land of Egypt.
I tell you the Four Questions you ask daddy and daddy's answer.
I tell you when to sip your wine and wash your hands and eat;
when to open the door for Elijah;
when to look for the afikomen;
and the songs to sing.

It's all in my pages.

After the seder is over, put me safely away until the seder next year.

I am the haggadah — the book about Passover.

Elijah The Prophet

In the middle of the table was a big silver cup filled with wine.

"That," mother said, "is for Elijah the Prophet."

"Is Elijah coming to the seder?" Dave said.

"Will Elijah drink up the wine?"

"Watch and see."

Dave watched.

Dave watched to see if Elijah drank from the big cup.

43

He watched while the door was opened for Elijah. He watched while the door was closed.

Was the wine in the cup all drunk up?

Was the wine in the cup half drunk up?

Was the wine in the cup a tiny bit drunk up?

"Well, Dave," mother said, bending over to look closer at the cup, "it doesn't look as if it was. But it's here for him if he ever should come. And anybody else who is hungry is welcome to come in and eat with us."

Moses

I am Moses, a prince of Egypt.

But I am also a Hebrew. An Egyptian princess found me when I was a baby. She took me to King Pharaoh's palace and brought me up as her own son.

But my people, the Hebrews, live in huts. They are slaves of Pharaoh.

They work hard for him, without rest.

And every day I hear them cry out because they work so hard.

They want to be free.

I must help them. I will go to Pharaoh and tell him to let my people be free.

Pharaoh

I am the king of Egypt, the Pharaoh.
I have many Hebrew slaves — thousands and thousands.
They work hard, building my pyramids.
Prince Moses tells me they do not want to be slaves. They want to go away and be free.
But if they go away, who will be my slaves? I will not let them go. I will make them work harder and harder. I will never let them go.

The Afikomen

Daddy hid the matzah called the afikomen. He hid it under baby Dan's plate.

After supper, Dave looked for it. He looked for it because if you find it daddy gives you a present.

But Dave couldn't find it. Neither could Judy.

"Now I'd like to go on with the seder," daddy said, "but where's the afikomen?"

Because he felt like it, baby Dan put his little hands under his plate and —

"Danny's got it!" cried Dave, rushing to him. "Yes, yes," shrieked Judy.

Dan waved the afikomen over his head and gave it to Dave.

"You *all* get presents," daddy said.

Dan didn't know what it was all about, but he was happy. He kept waving his fists.

45

When It's Passover, It's—Spring!

All week of Passover, Dave and Judy ate matzoth.

They ate matzah pancakes,
   and matzah puddings,
   and matzah dumplings,
   and other matzah goodies.

"Matzoth reminds us," Dave said, "of the time the Jews were slaves."

"I know," Judy said, "but they got free."

On the last morning of Passover the children dressed in their bright new clothes and started out for the synagogue.

And they noticed how green the grass was getting,
   and they saw a robin pulling up
   a worm,
   and buds that had burst open on
   the trees.

Dave took a deep breath as he walked, and so did Judy.

"When it's Passover," Dave said, "it's spring!"

A Sleepy Little Boy

There was once a little boy who wanted to know things.

"Why do we eat matzoth?" he asked. "Why do you lean on a cushion, daddy? Why do we eat bitter herbs? And why do we dip them?"

"This is why and that is why," daddy said, and he read why from the haggadah.

And while he read why, the little boy listened—
and sipped three more glasses of wine,
and ate his supper,
and sang Had Gad Yoh and Addir Hu,
and tried to keep his eyes open,
and fell asleep,
and was carried up to bed.

Now do you know why, my sleepy little boy?

Lag Be-Omer

Did you ever hear of Bar Kokba? He was also called Bar Kokba the Brave, Bar Kokba the Strong, Bar Kokba Son of a Star. He lived in Palestine, long long ago.

Now at that time Palestine was not free, because a Roman king ruled over the land.

But Bar Kokba wanted Palestine to be free—and so did many other Jews.

So they fought with bow and arrow against the Roman army, fighting from caves and hills, just as the Maccabees had once fought.

Bar Kokba lost the war.

He lost the war, but we always remember him and the many brave men who fought to make Palestine free.

We remember them all on the holiday called Lag Be-Omer.

Here Comes Bar Kokba

"Here I go!" called Dave.

"Where—where are you going?" said Judy.

"To the fields and the hills and the caves. To shoot my bow and arrows. Like Bar Kokba. Want to be my horse?"

"Sure," Judy said.

And away they galloped.

47

First Flowers

Every morning Judy went out to look at her seedlings.

But she was worried.

"Do you think they'll bloom in time?" she asked Dave.

"In time for what?"

"Shabuoth."

"Who knows!"

And when she saw the little blue crocuses coming out here and there on the front lawn— and not her seedlings—she was still worried.

Every morning Judy looked at her seedlings. Sometimes she watered them. Sometimes she brushed a pebble away from a stem, or tucked in the soil around a tiny root.

One morning it rained hard and then the sun smiled so warmly afterwards that Judy went out without her coat. That day she saw a white tulip had opened and a purple pansy face.

"Dave!" she called, running into the house. "They're blooming. My flowers are blooming!"

"And did you see my shrubs!" he said.

Every day more flowers and shrubs bloomed and, on the afternoon before Shabouth, Judy and Dave went out with scissors and clippers. Judy snipped off some pansies and daffodils and tulips and lilies-of-the-valley. Dave clipped off some of the lilacs and a little branch of the flowering dogwood.

Together they carried the first flowers they had gathered to the synagogue, to decorate it for the holiday.

That Shabuoth Evening

"Mm . . . how fragrant!" father said when he came home and smelled the lilacs and the other flowers on the table.

"They're home-made," mother said, laughing.

"Out of our garden—? *Can't* be."

"Yes they ARE!" cried Judy and Dave, giggling.

"Beautiful!" he said, swooping up the children and giving them a big, loving hug.

After the kiddush and the dairy supper of blintzes, mother said, "You should have seen all the flowers and shrubs they took to the synagogue. It really made one think of the harvest gifts the people used to bring to the Temple in Jerusalem."

"Oh, daddy, I forgot!" Judy said, suddenly. "Cousin Sandra is going to be confirmed tomorrow and she invited me. May I go to the temple?"

"Certainly," he said. "We're all going ."

Confirmation

The temple was crowded.

The choir sang and everybody stood up.

Down the aisle came Sandra with the other confirmands, all dressed in white gowns.

One girl went up to the pulpit and read the Ten Commandments. A boy read something else from the Bible.

Then Sandra said a poem she had made up herself.

"We promise to be good Jews," she said in her poem.

A boy gave a talk he had made up himself.

"We promise to follow the teachings of the Torah," he said in his talk.

After each confirmand had spoken, the rabbi stood up. He said he was proud of them, and happy they were going to keep on with their studies. He then blessed them and gave each girl and boy a Bible.

After the service, there was much kissing and handshaking. Some mothers couldn't keep back their tears. Everybody congratulated the parents as well as the confirmands. "Mazel tov! What a young *lady* your Deborah is!" "What a fine son you have!" "How lovely!" "How smart!"

Judy hugged Sandra. She was so proud of her. She thought her cousin was the smartest and loveliest of all the confirmands.

Their Own Play

Dave and Judy saw the Shabuoth play in school but they had not acted in it. So when they got home, Dave said:

"I am Moses and I am going up the mountain for the Ten Commandments." He climbed up on the living room couch. "And the people are waiting down below—"

"Me," said Judy. "I'm the people. I'm waiting."

"Don't worry, O People," said Dave. "I will bring you the Commandments pretty soon."

"Don't be too long," said Judy.

"Boom, boom," shouted Dave. "I am making thunder and lightnings and rainings and snowing and hailings and the whole mountain is shaking and—"

Judy held her ears.

"—and here they are—no, no—wait! If I bring you the Commandments, will you keep them, O People?"

"Yes," said Judy.

"Will you let your children keep them, too?"

"Oh, yes," said Judy.

"Will you let everybody in the whole world keep them?"

"Certainly."

"Even bad people who want to be good—?"

"Of course."

"Then—*here*—*they*—ARE!" he said, jumping from the couch. "Here they are—the Tablets of the Law."

"Lovely!" said Judy.

"See what they say? They say you must tell the truth—"

"*I* tell the truth," said Judy.

"—and you mustn't kill anybody—"

"*I* never kill anybody—oh! I killed an ant before—only it was an accident: I stepped on him."

"—and you mustn't ever steal or do things like that. And you must be good to your mother and your father—"

"I *love* daddy and mommy," said Judy.

At that moment mother came in from the kitchen.

"Oh my darlings!" she said, kissing them both." I *know* you love us. And we love *you*—more than anything in the world."